Beyond the Pale
of Vengeance

by

KAN KIKUCHI

Translated from the Japanese by

REV. JISHŌ PERRY, M.O.B.C., *and*

KIMIKO VAGO

❧ SHASTA ABBEY PRESS
MT. SHASTA, CALIFORNIA

First edition—1998
© 1998 Santa Barbara Buddhist Priory
All rights reserved.

This manuscript may not be copied or reproduced
in any way without the written permission of the
copyright holder.

Santa Barbara Buddhist Priory
1115 Tunnel Road
Santa Barbara, CA 93105
(805) 898-0848

Printed in the United States of America.

This book is published with permission of the
author's family. An earlier serialized version appeared in
The Journal of the Order of Buddhist Contemplatives.

ISBN 0-930066-19-7
LIBRARY OF CONGRESS CARD CATALOG NUMBER: 98-60595

This book is dedicated to my teacher, Rev. Master P.T.N.H. Jiyu-Kennett, founder of the Order of Buddhist Contemplatives and first Abbess of Shasta Abbey. Born January 1, 1924, died November 6, 1996.

For 34 years her life as a monk and her example in Buddhist training inspired hundreds of monks and lay people to begin Buddhist practice, take the Buddhist Precepts and find very real solutions to the problems of suffering.

PORTRAIT OF REV. MASTER JIYU-KENNETT,
PAINTED BY REV. MOKUGEN KUBLICKI, M.O.B.C.

"The light of the Buddha is increasing in brilliance and the wheel of the Dharma is always turning."

ACKNOWLEDGEMENTS

We wish to thank all those who have helped
in the production of this book.

Contents

Introduction   vii

Chapter One   1

Chapter Two   7

Chapter Three   19

Chapter Four   38

A Note About Ao-no-Domon   57
Photos   60
About the Order of Buddhist Contemplatives   62
About the Monasteries of the Order   63
About the Santa Barbara Buddhist Priory   64

Introduction

One of the basic teachings of Buddhism is that change is a fundamental fact of all existence. Not only do all things change by their very nature, but the very fortunate part of being born as a human being is that we can <u>choose</u> to change. No matter what kind of behavior we have manifested in the past, we are not bound by any force to continue that behavior now or in the future. We have complete and total free will. Most of the time we choose to be dominated by old habits of greed, anger and delusion. These habits have created suffering which we now experience, but we can always choose to change these habits. Everyone has an intuitive sense of the Eternal; we instinctively know what is "right" to do, even though it may be difficult to do it. When we do things that cause harm to ourselves or others, when we refuse to change or persist in old, unsatisfactory habits, this creates suffering. As human beings we can experience suffering, but we can also know enlightenment, or experience the direct knowledge of the Unborn, the Undying, i.e., That Which is Eternal.

The story told in *Beyond the Pale of Vengeance* shows how a man can commit the great crimes of murder and robbery and yet is able to completely turn his life around, and know the greatest fulfillment: the direct experience of the Eternal, the Buddha Nature, and then to completely commit his life to selfless service thereafter. Having caused harm to others, not to mention the damage done to himself, he can still find a way to be of service to others and in the process "clean up" the karmic consequences created by the former actions. In Buddhist teaching, karma is the law of cause and effect on a moral and spiritual realm. We create karma by the choices we make in our thoughts, words and actions. When those choices are motivated by greed, anger, fear, impatience, pride, jealousy, etc., the consequences are experienced in the form of suffering. Suffering is not primarily experienced as physical pain, it is more likely to be manifested in wanting things to be 'other' than they are. This is experienced in the feeling of disquiet, dissatisfaction, despair or uneasiness that results from unenlightened action. We seek comfort in relation-ships, wealth, jobs, social status, fame, worldly success, sensual pleasures, alcohol, drugs, intellec-tual learning, external comforts, or anything else we imagine will give us some sense of wholeness, adequacy or peace of mind. These things, however, cannot provide us with adequacy, because we are already whole and complete. We are not separate from the Eternal, or the Buddha Nature. But until we learn how to act on our wholeness and find a purpose in our lives that is bigger than the pursuit of selfish ends, we cannot **know** this adequacy or have genuine peace of mind.

In Buddhist training we can experience di-rectly That Which is Eternal; the emphasis is placed on dedicating our lives for the benefit of all living things. In the practice of Buddhist meditation we learn how to sit still enough to listen to that intuitive sense of the Eternal within our own hearts. We practice restraining our greeds, angers and fears. At the same time we learn how to embrace and accept the suffering that our previous actions have created; we try to change the old habits that have resulted in suffering and learn how to put our actions in har-mony with something bigger than self-interest. As explained in the *Scripture of Great Wisdom:* "When one is truly one with wisdom great, the obstacles dissolve." This is a constant ongoing process: "O Buddha, going, going, going on beyond, and always going on beyond, always BECOMING Buddha. Hail! Hail! Hail"* The process of training itself expresses enlightenment.

It is very difficult for people in our culture to imagine that it is possible to treat ourselves and others with complete respect no matter what previous crimes we or others have committed. Each person will get the results of these actions in the form of karmic consequences, which are manifested as feelings. The suffering produced is not there to punish but to teach. If people are treated with respect, they are much more likely to learn how to avoid the same mistakes in the future than if they are faced with judgmental, punitive or vengeful attitudes.

The story told here in *Beyond the Pale of Vengeance* is based on the life of an actual monk

---

* *The Liturgy of the Order of Buddhist Contemplatives for the Laity,* comp. P.T.N.H. Jiyu-Kennett, 2nd ed. rev. (Mt. Shasta, California: Shasta Abbey Press, 1990), p. 74.

who lived during the 18th century in Japan and shows how even a killer can become a fine example of Buddhist practice. In completely changing his own attitudes and behavior he was able to help himself and others to convert greeds, angers and fears into compassion, love and wisdom. It is very similar to the story of Angulimala, who, during the life of the Buddha, had killed nearly 1000 people. After meeting the Buddha and discovering that there was a way to solve the problem of suffering, he became a sincere and devoted monk. He was afterwards stoned by villagers who could not believe he had truly changed and feared him because of his prior criminal activity. When he died, he was at peace within himself, and respected and embraced by the Buddha who explained that the consequences of his former actions had been completely converted; in accepting his death with an open heart feeling neither anger nor fear, he could be free from the old karmic habits and debts. After his death the Buddha explained to his disciples that Angulimala had entered into parinirvana. There was no residue of karmic consequences from his life as a murderer left to be reborn. He had completely "cleaned up" the old karma and left no suffering to be converted.

In the interests of accuracy, it is important to note that Kan Kikuchi, the author of *Beyond the Pale of Vengeance*, wrote a novel based on historical fact. That the historical facts may not be exactly the same as recounted in his story does not detract from the spiritual accuracy of the teachings that, at least for me as editor and a Buddhist monk, is the important aspect of this story. In the Note at the end of this book is contained information about the historical priest and the building of the tunnel that may differ somewhat from the impression given by the author in this story. There is a wonderful Buddhist teaching that says: "The Truth does not insist on Truth." In the context of this story it means that the truth of the spiritual message is more important than concern over historical accuracy.

It is from our own personal efforts in religious training that we can find and experience freedom from suffering for ourselves. We may not have killed or robbed anyone, but all of us have broken the Precepts, by having acted on other forms of anger, stealing, greed, dishonesty, pride, contempt for others or disrespect that have caused harm to ourselves and others. It is also important to know that we are no better and no worse than those who have killed or robbed. All beings have the Buddha Nature, and all will receive the results of former actions. In order to 'clean up' the consequences of past karmic misdeeds, we do not need to be the victim of an angry mob or go out and build tunnels by hand through rock cliffs, but all of us must find a way that is appropriate for ourselves in the circumstances of our lives to change the habits of ignorance into selfless giving. Although each person must find his or her own way to be successful, I, personally, know of no better way to do this than sincere commitment to Buddhist practice. It is not enough to read or think about this. What is important is to make sincere changes in our attitudes and actions. Perhaps this story will inspire modern readers to deepen their own practice, take Refuge in the Buddha, the Dharma and the Sangha, and find a selfless purpose to work for the benefit of all living beings.

REV. JISHŌ PERRY, M.O.B.C.

Beyond the Pale
of Vengeance

Chapter One

Unable to avoid the master's sword, Ichikuro received a shallow cut from his left cheek to his chin. Knowing he had had the unlawful affair with his master's favorite concubine, he offered no resistance to the attack. He tried to avoid the sword without any intention of fighting back. Bewildered by the sudden attack, he was not ready to give up his life over this sexual escapade, and he tried to evade the flashing sword. After accusing him of the infidelity, the master suddenly lashed out at him; instinctively he grabbed a nearby candlestick, which was the only thing available to defend himself against the master's sharp sword. Although the master was nearly fifty years old, he was still physically fit and a strong person. The attack was sudden and violent. Ichikuro was hesitant to attack the older man and was confused by his own shame for his part in the affair. He failed to adequately defend himself and received the wound on his face.

When he saw his own blood, his mind suddenly switched. Previously subdued, he became as wild as a wounded bull. He was threatened with immediate death, and all the cultural conditioning of restraint and respect for the master's authority disappeared. He saw his master as a wild beast threatening his life. Ichikuro instinctively went on the attack. With a shout of anger he hurled the candlestick at his master's face. Since Ichikuro had initially defended himself so feebly, Master Saburobei was unconcerned for his own protection. Caught off guard by the sudden attack, he failed to evade the flying candlestick which struck him forcefully on the right eye. As the master staggered back, Ichikuro quickly moved forward, pulling out his dagger.

"How dare you, peon, attack me!" cried the enraged Saburobei. Silently, Ichikuro attacked again. Although the master's sword was three feet long and the vassal's only a foot long, they clashed furiously. As they struggled for their lives, slashing at each other, the master's sword kept hitting the low ceiling which prevented him from effectively controlling his weapon. Ichikuro used this to his own advantage. The master recognized his disadvantage and tried to move the fight outside. Stepping back, he went out to the covered walkway. Ichikuro still had the advantage. The master became frustrated and lashed out with a wild shout. Overcome with anger, he lost control. The sword missed its intended victim and stuck deeply into the door frame. "Damn it!" thought Saburobei. As he struggled to free his sword, Ichikuro lunged, slashing open his master's side.

As soon as Saburobei fell from the mortal wound, Ichikuro awoke to the reality of the situation. Previously clouded by the emotional intensity of the fight, his mind cleared, and he realized he had committed the capital offense of murdering his master. Overwhelmed by remorse and fear, he felt drained of vitality. It was late in the evening. The fight had taken place in the main house away from the servants' quarters and no one had heard the violent struggle except for the maids who lived in the main house. The maids huddled together in a room, paralyzed with fear.

Ichikuro was overwhelmed with deep shame and regret. Although the young samurai had wasted his time with women, alcohol and gambling, he had not, until now, committed any serious offense. He had never even considered committing the treasonable crime of killing his master.*

As he contemplated the bloody sword still clutched in his hand, he could think only of his worthlessness. He thought about the sexual affair with his master's concubine, his refusal to accept the consequences for this behavior, his attack on his master, and now his master's death. Looking at the master's wounded body in the last throes of twitching as he lay dying, he calmly resolved to do the honorable thing and take his own life. Suddenly a voice, from the adjoining room, broke in on the now intensely silent murder scene.

"Oh! Was I worried! What was going to happen? I was sure that my turn would be next as soon as he cut you. I was hiding here behind the screen too scared to breathe. This is truly fortunate! We'd better hurry now. We'll need to steal the money and make our escape. Nobody knows what has happened yet. We need to be quick, if we plan to escape.

---

* The eight treasonable or capital offenses: rebellion, treason, immoral acts, infidelity, breach of the duties of filial piety, offenses against the government [emperor or shogun], offenses of extreme disrespect, and other serious crimes.

The maids and the nanny are shivering in fear in the kitchen. I'll go and tell them to stay quiet for their own protection. Please search for the money." The voice quivered slightly, suppressing her fear with a show of confidence.

Ichikuro, who had lost his will to live, became energized by the sound of this woman's voice. He arose like a puppet propelled by the will of this strong woman. He opened the tea cupboard and grabbed the tea vessels, leaving his bloody hand print on the pale white paulownia wood surface. He started searching for money hidden in the drawers. When the woman, Oyumi, his master's favorite concubine, returned, he had only found one package with the equivalent of five 'ryo' pieces in silver coins of two 'shugin.' Oyumi saw the money when she came in from the kitchen. She said disdainfully: "This is nothing." She started rifling the drawers herself. Finally she searched the chest where the armor was stored, but came up empty-handed.

Then she said: "He's such a stingy miser, he must have hidden the money in jars and buried them in the garden." She was disgusted. Quickly she wrapped up some fine clothing and and an expensive medicine box in a large cloth.

The two lovers fled from the house of Nakagawa Saburobei, a direct vassal of the shogun, who
had lived in the town of Asakusa Tawara.* It was
the early fall in the third year of An'ei. They left behind the three-year-old Jitsunosuke, the only child
of Saburobei, asleep in his nanny's arms, oblivious
to his father's murder.

* This was in Edo, now modern Tokyo.

Chapter Two

Ichikuro and Oyumi fled south from Edo. They avoided taking the main road, the Tokaido, and used the mountain road, the Tosando, where they would be less likely to be seen. Ichikuro repeatedly felt pangs of conscience over the killing of his master, while Oyumi was far less sensitive for she had hardened herself by starting life in a tea house of dubious reputation. Whenever Ichikuro was downcast she would tell him: "It is futile to worry about the actions of the past. You're already a criminal. Cheer up and enjoy yourself." With this kind of encouragement he was able to continue his life of criminal activities.

After leaving Shinshu they arrived at Yabuhara, the overnight rest town in Kiso. They had nearly spent all their money, leaving them only a few small coins. Since they were broke, they decided to solve their financial dilemma with criminal activities. At first Oyumi would entice a man into a sexual encounter and then Ichikuro would come in and extort money from their victim. From Shinshu to Bishu at each of the overnight rest towns they would extort the travelers' expenses from farmers and townsmen. At the beginning Ichikuro went along with these criminal activities at Oyumi's instigation; soon, however, he began to savor these adventures. Since he wore the clothing of a masterless samurai, his victims would obediently submit even to robberies, because they had been taught to fear and respect the samurai. As he became more familiar with these criminal activities, his confidence grew, and he found it easier just to rob people straight out. Eventually he came to feel that killing and robbing were a perfectly acceptable livelihood.

Subsequently they settled down in the mountains at the Torii Pass between Shinano and Kiso. They opened a tea house where he worked during the day and from which he left to rob travelers at night. He soon adapted to this lifestyle and became comfortable with it. He concentrated his attacks on wealthy looking travelers. After killing them, he became clever at safely disposing of the corpses. He only had to do this three or four times a year in order to make a decent living at it.

In the spring of the third year since Ichikuro and Oyumi left Edo, the highways were crowded with people. Although this rarely happened, two processions of Daimyo, feudal lords and their retinue, from the northern prefectures passed by on their obligatory visits to the Shogun in Edo.* There were also a considerable number of pilgrims going to and from the shrine at Ise, some from Shinshu, others from as far away as Echigo and Ecchu. Some of these travelers extended their journeys to Kyoto and Osaka. Ichikuro wanted to kill two or three of these travelers to secure his expenses for the year. Along the Kiso highway the wild cherry blossoms could be seen among the cedars and cypress trees, but they were starting to fall. It was the end of the cherry blossom season which meant that soon the travelers would be less frequent.

One evening two travelers, a man and a woman, stopped at Ichikuro's tea house. They were obviously a married couple, the husband in his early thirties and the wife of twenty-three or twenty-four. They gave the appearance of wealthy farmers from

---

* During the Tokagawa Shogunates, the Daimyo were required to present themselves at court every other year.

Shinshu, traveling for pleasure without any servants. When Ichikuro saw how they were dressed, he decided to rob them.

"It cannot be far to the town of Yabuhara, can it?" asked the husband, as he stopped to retie the strings of his sandals in front of the tea house. Before Ichikuro could respond, Oyumi appeared from the kitchen and said: "Indeed, Sir, it is very close, less than a mile. Please relax and rest awhile."

When Ichikuro heard these words of deception, he realized that Oyumi had already conceived the idea of robbing this couple. The actual distance to Yabuhara was five times greater than the one Oyumi had told them. It was a scheme that he had frequently used to catch travelers off guard. He would suggest that the distance was short, then the travelers would rest until late in the day, and he would run down a short cut and assault them in the dark as they approached the entrance to Yabuhara. Since the young husband felt assured, he replied: "Well then, we'll take some tea." They had already fallen for the bait. The wife untied the red strings of her straw hat, removed it, and sat down close to her husband. They rested there recovering from the exertion of climbing to the top of the pass. When they had paid for their tea and started down along the Torii Pass road to the Ogiso Valley, the sky was turning into a purple sunset.

As soon as they had disappeared, Oyumi gave Ichikuro the signal. He strapped on his short sword and sprinted after them like a hunter pursuing his prey. He soon turned off to the right of the main road, taking a steep shortcut along the Kiso River.

When Ichikuro reached the tree lined road leading to the Yabuhara Station, the long spring evening had died and the nearly full moon was rising behind the Kiso mountains, outlining the Kiso mountains in soft moonlight. Hiding himself behind one of the willow trees that lined the road, Ichikuro waited patiently for the couple to arrive. Deep within his heart, he knew it was evil to kill these two happy travelers. He was loath to disappoint Oyumi's expectations, however, so he dismissed the idea of aborting his plans and returning home empty-handed.

Still, however, he felt uneasy and was reluctant to spill the blood of this young couple. He hoped that they would simply obey his command for money and clothes. He made up his mind not to kill them as long as they submitted to his demand without a struggle.

Just as he made this decision, he saw the couple walking briskly along the highway. They seemed very tired from the unexpectedly long distance of the journey. They approached quickly, silently supporting one another as they walked.

When they reached the willow tree, Ichikuro suddenly jumped out, blocking their path and uttering his usual threats. The travelers were surprised and frightened. The man pulled out a small traveling sword and shielded his wife behind him. Ichikuro was slightly caught off guard initially, but recovered his composure and shouted: "Hey traveler, if you try to fight me, you'll die. Just give me your money and your clothes and you can go away unharmed." The traveler studied Ichikuro's face and then exclaimed: "Oh! You are the owner of the tea house, aren't you!" He then lunged at Ichikuro to attack him. Ichikuro realized that he no longer had a choice to let them live; it would endanger the safety of both himself and Oyumi. Ichikuro skillfully dodged the blow and successfully slashed the man's neck, killing him instantly. He then noticed the wife trembling in fear, crouching by the roadside ready to submit to any demand.

Ichikuro did not want to kill this woman, but he was sure he would die if he did not. He realized he had to act now while still churning with emotion from the fight. He lifted his sword above his head to strike. The woman clasped her hand in reverence, begging him for mercy. Looking into her eyes, he hesitated. However, he knew he had to kill her. Then greed arose within him, and he realized that if he killed her with his sword it would leave blood stains on the beautiful clothes. He grabbed, instead, the towel from his waist band and quickly strangled her.

After killing these two, he was suddenly overcome by fear and remorse. He felt he had to get out of there immediately. In a panic he snatched the waistbands, where they kept the money, pulled off their clothing and fled from the murder scene as fast as he could. Although he had killed more than ten people before, they had all been silver-haired old men, merchants or tradesmen only. He had never before killed a young couple, both man and wife together, with his own hands.

Tortured by these pangs of conscience, he returned home. As soon as he opened the door, he threw the clothes and money down at Oyumi as if they were contaminated. Calmly she first checked the money which was far less than she had expected. It was barely more than twenty 'ryo.' Then she started to examine the woman's clothes. Oyumi said "Oh goody! This kimono is very expensive and so is the under kimono. But where are the woman's hair ornaments?" She gave Ichikuro an accusing look and silently demanded an explanation.

"Hair ornaments?" he asked in a daze.

"Yes, you idiot! Hair ornaments! She would not have had imitation combs and pins if she was wearing such fine clothing. When she removed her hat earlier while having tea, I noticed that they were definitely tortoiseshell," said Oyumi yelling at him. Ichikuro was emotionally devastated by the murders and had not given the slightest thought to the hair comb and pins. He stood in stunned silence.

"Don't tell me you forgot them! If they are tortoiseshell, they'll be worth at least seven or eight 'ryo'. You're no amateur. Why did you kill these people? You idiot! What do you think you are doing, killing such a well dressed woman and leaving behind her hair ornaments? How long have you been robbing people? Only an idiot would make such a stupid mistake. Well, what do you have to say for yourself!" The commanding Oyumi glared at Ichikuro with scorn.

Because he was already overcome with remorse for having killed the young couple, Oyumi's words stung like salt on a wound. Ichikuro felt no regret at having forgotten to take the hair ornaments. He felt no regret for his incompetence as a robber. He had been so upset by the emotional impact of the killings that he had completely lost his head and gave no thought to the fact that the woman had been wearing valuable hair ornaments. Even now under Oyumi's scornful glare, he could not bring himself to feel any regret for the oversight. Although he had been reduced to robbery and murder for profit, he had not sunk to the level of a demonic ogre sucking marrow from the bones of the dead.

Oyumi, however, with insatiable greed, could not be satisfied with the murder of the young woman, nor with her money or fine clothing, she could think of nothing but the missing hair ornaments. Ichikuro started to feel deep resentment and anger rising up within him toward Oyumi. Caught up in her own lust for wealth, Oyumi was quite oblivious to the emotional change that Ichikuro was undergoing.

"Now, run along! Go fetch them immediately! What's the point in going to all the trouble of killing someone and not getting the rewards?" she said triumphantly.

Ichikuro remained silent and unresponsive.

"Oh my! I've hit a sensitive nerve! Your feelings are hurt because I accused you of incompetence. Well! Why are you not going! Are you just going to throw away ten pieces of gold?" Repeatedly, Oyumi prodded Ichikuro.

Normally Ichikuro would have leapt at her command, but his mind was in deep confusion. He was starting to recognize the karmic consequences for his criminal activity and was so deeply engrossed in thought that he could barely hear her.

"Since you refuse to go no matter how many times I ask, I'll just have to do it myself. Where are they? In the usual place?" asked Oyumi.

An irresistible disgust for Oyumi was arising in Ichikuro, and he felt glad at the prospect of being rid of her, if only for a moment.

"Where else would they be? They are on the tree lined road just before Yabuhara," said Ichikuro contemptuously.

"Well then, I'll just run along down there myself. Lucky there's a bright moon tonight! What a bungler you are!" she responded.

Tucking up the skirt of her kimono and strapping on some straw sandals, she took off down the hill.

As Ichikuro saw Oyumi leaving, he was overwhelmed by disgust. Watching the woman running off in a frenzy to remove hair ornaments from a corpse, he felt an uncontrollable loathing made more poignant by the fact that he had once loved her. Whenever he had committed a crime, he was able to justify the action in his own mind because it had a purpose for him. Now that he could see the rapacious greed reflected in Oyumi's actions, he was deeply disturbed by the truth of his own behavior. With horror, he realized the depth of his own responsibility.

He saw the woman for whom he had risked his life disgracing the dignity and beauty of her gender by running off to the corpse of the murdered woman like a jackal on a carcass, all for some tortoiseshell ornaments worth only a few pieces of gold. He could no longer stand to spend another minute with this woman in this evil place.

As he began to realize this, the memories of all his past evil deeds welled up in him, stinging his conscience. The eyes of the strangled woman, the groans of the silk merchant covered in blood, the screams of the white-haired old man dying of a stab wound: all rose up together to confront his conscience. His first reaction was to escape from his past actions as soon as possible, and even to run away from himself. Most of all he wanted to get away from the woman whom he saw as the instigator of his crimes. He stood up determined to leave. He packed a few possessions. Snatching up the cash from the man he'd just robbed, he ran outside before he had all his clothes on.

He had only run a few yards when he realized that everything he owned was stolen. He ran back to the tea house and with all his might flung the money and clothes against the door frame. To avoid meeting Oyumi, he ran along the Kiso River taking a little used side path. He had no idea where he was going. He just wanted to get as far away as possible from the place he saw as the source of his crimes.

Chapter Three

Ichikuro ran over mountains and through fields for over fifty miles without stopping. On the next day right after noon, he reached Joganji, a Buddhist Temple in the suburb of Ogaki, in Mino Prefecture. He had no intention of coming to this temple. It was only by accident in his haste to escape that he arrived here. He felt a deep need to confess and offer up his past criminal actions when the idea of seeking the light of compassion in religion arose within him.

Joganji was the head temple for the Shingon sect in Mino Prefecture. Clutching the sleeve of the great priest, Myohen, the abbot of the temple, Ichikuro made a sincere act of contrition and confession. The old priest did not reject this man, although he confessed to many horrible crimes. When Ichikuro proposed to give himself up to the legal authorities, the old priest stopped him and said: "Since you have committed many serious crimes, the authorities will most surely hang you. If that happens you, most likely, will be reborn in hell and suffer great punishment for a very long time. Instead, you have the opportunity to take refuge in the Buddha, the Dharma and the Sangha, abandon your selfish ways and dedicate your life to the self-less service of working for the good of all living things—including yourself. This is important!" Hearing these compassionate words of Buddhist teaching and realizing the depth of genuine concern the old monk held out to him, Ichikuro was deeply moved in his heart to work for the good of all living things. He immediately decided to become a monk and enter the Sangha. He asked for ordination. The old monk consented to do the ceremony, shaving his head and giving him the Buddhist Precepts and the ordination name, "Ryokai."

Ichikuro gave himself up to the practice of Buddhism wholeheartedly. Because his desire to know the Truth was sincere, within six months he was able to directly experience the purity and immaculacy of the Unborn. In the morning he threw himself eagerly into the esoteric practices of the three actions of body, speech and mind. In the evening he devoted himself completely to the meditation of calling on the aid of the Amida Buddha. These two practices quickly bore great fruit from which the seed of wisdom sprouted. His faith became unshakable, and it was not long before his master recognized him as a full priest. He sought and obtained permission to venture out of the monastery on a pilgrimage as a wandering mendicant monk with the great vow of the Bodhisattva to work for the good of all living things.

He left Mino and went first to the capital at Kyoto. Although now a priest, he still experienced great suffering; foremost in his mind were feelings that he was unworthy of life after having killed so many people. He deeply desired to expiate his criminal acts and atone for them by doing all he could to help others, even if only in a very small way. Especially when he saw travelers, he remembered the harm he had caused to the travelers in the Kiso mountains. He felt he was bearing an irreparable burden for all travelers.

No matter what he was doing, day or night, he ceaselessly thought about helping others. Whenever he saw anyone on the road who might need assistance, he would offer his hand to pull them along or get behind them and push. If he came across anyone who was weak with illness, old age or youth, he would carry them on his back, even for long distances. Whenever he came upon a broken bridge on some back road, he would go to the hills, fell the necessary trees and cut the timbers, find the appropriate stones and make the repairs. If he saw a pothole in the road, he would fetch sand and gravel and make the repair. Throughout Kinki and Chugoku he made continual efforts to do good deeds.

Whenever he thought about his past actions, the enormity of the harm caused seemed higher than heaven, while the triviality of his good deeds seemed lower than the earth itself. The more he thought about his old karma, the heavier became the burden. As he contemplated this, his mind darkened. He would wake up in the night in an inn and feel ashamed to be alive after having committed such horrible crimes. He seriously considered suicide. Whenever the darkness of despair arose, he would remind himself of his spiritual purpose and pray for the time when he had the opportunity to work for the good of all living things.

In the autumn of the ninth year of the Kyoho era (1724), Ryokai traveled from Akamagaseki

across the channel to Kohura on Kyushu Island. He
visited the shrine of Usa Hachimangu in Buzen
Prefecture. From there he traveled south from
Yokkaichi, passing through fields of red clay head-
ing for Rakanji Temple by traveling up the valley of
the Yamakuni River.

The autumn in Tsukushi deepened at every
town where he stayed the night. The wax trees
stood out in bright crimson in contrast to the other
trees in the forest. The rice was ripe, and its yellow
color brightened the fields. The orange of the per-
simmon, for which the area was famous, decorated
the eaves of the farmhouses.

One fine fall day while he kept the clear waters
of the Yamakuni River sparkling in the morning sun
off to his right, he took the mountain path up the
Hotokezaka Pass from Mikuchi. He reached the
town of Hida about noon. It was a quiet town, and
he took out his monk's bowl and begged for his mid-
day meal as was usual for traveling monks. Then he
headed south along the Yamakuni Valley. After he
left Hida, the road returned to run along the river,
and he crossed through an area of volcanic rock.

Ryokai was using his priest's staff to steady
himself on the difficult stony path when he came

upon four or five farmers standing in a group making a commotion. As Ryokai approached, one of the farmers spotted him and said: "Your arrival is auspicious because there is a man here who has just met with a violent death. Please give him a proper funeral and recite scriptures for his benefit, since you arrived at such a perfect time."

When he heard the words 'violent death,' he immediately thought of the death of travelers killed by robbers and remembered the evil deeds of his past; his legs began to tremble, and he felt overcome with remorse.

"He looks as if he drowned. But why are his skin and flesh so badly torn up?" asked Ryokai in a trembling voice.

"Reverend Sir, you seem to be a traveler and you are probably not familiar with the area. About fifty yards further up this path there is a very dangerous place called the 'chain bridge.' It's the most dangerous place in the Yamakuni Valley. Every man or horse going north or south must be very careful passing over it. This man was a pack-horse driver who lived up the river in the village of Kakizaka. This morning while crossing the 'chain bridge' his horse became frightened and shied. They both fell, head over heels, over fifty feet down the cliff and died this violent death," one of the farmers replied.

"I have heard about the dangers of the 'chain bridge,'" said Ryokai with great sympathy. "Does this kind of accident happen often?" he asked as he looked at the mutilated corpse.

"Maybe three or four times a year. There are many, as many as ten in a year, who meet their deaths in accidents like this. Because it is so dangerous, repairs cannot be made easily when it is damaged by wind and rain," replied the farmer. As the farmers prepared to bury the body, Ryokai performed the funeral and recited scriptures for the benefit of the dead man. Then he hurried off to the 'chain bridge' after the ceremony. It was just up the road where he saw the rocky cliff rising up on the left side of the river, over one hundred feet of grey, barren volcanic rock split open with deep crevices. The water of the Yamakuni River seemed drawn to the base of this cliff and swirled in a menacing whirlpool of deep green.

He realized that this was the infamous 'chain bridge' which the farmers had been talking about. The pathway was cut in two about halfway up the cliff by a rickety bridge made of pine and cedar logs chained together. You would not have to be an old woman or a child to be terrified at the prospect of crossing this bridge, looking down about fifty feet above the swirling river with one hundred feet of solid rock cliff towering above. Clinging to the cliff and carefully maneuvering across the rickety bridge on trembling legs, he managed to get across safely. Looking back upon the cliff, suddenly he was deeply moved by a profound thought rising from his very heart.

Feeling that all his previous efforts to atone for his past crimes had been petty and incomplete, he had prayed for a challenge to fulfill a mighty purpose. When he saw this extremely difficult pass where many travelers had died, it was only natural that he was willing to risk his life to find a solution to this challenging problem. He felt a fearless resolve arise from his heart to cut a tunnel, four hundred yards long, through this solid rock cliff. Ryokai realized that this situation was the answer to his prayers. If he could save ten people in one year, he could save one hundred people in ten years. It struck him that over the course of one hundred years, or even a thousand years, countless thousands would be saved by such a tunnel.

As soon as he formulated this plan, he immediately started to put it into action. He threw himself wholeheartedly into the work. He immediately moved into the priests' quarters of Rakanji Temple and started asking the local villagers if they would be willing to help raise money for the great work of making a tunnel through the cliff. None of the locals believed this strange priest who had come out of nowhere.

"Only a madman would come up with such a crazy scheme to cut a tunnel, four hundred yards long, through that cliff. Ha, ha, ha....," laughed some with a derisive tone. They were the kind ones.

Others were less kind and accused him of being a fraud: "A great imposter! You might as well believe he'll take us to the moon. Only a con man would try to collect money for such an impossible task," so they said and actively tried to prevent his even asking for contributions.

For ten days he vainly tried to solicit contributions. Seeing that no one believed him, he decided to do the work himself. He managed to get a stonemason's hammer and chisel and stood at one end of the great cliff. It was a comic picture. Although volcanic rock was not difficult to chip, the idea of one man cutting through a great long cliff towering above the river was ridiculous.

The village people laughed and pointed at the priest saying: "At last he must have gone mad!" Ryokai, however, was undaunted. He bathed in the clear waters of the Yamakuni River and prayed to Kanzeon, the Bodhisattva of Compassion, and with all his might brought down the first blow of his hammer. Only two or three chips flew out of the rock. When he put all his strength into the second blow, only a few chips flew out of the immense rock. For a third, fourth and fifth time Ryokai's hammer came down with all his strength.

When he was hungry, he would visit the neighboring village and beg for his meal. When he had eaten, he returned to the cliff and continued to chip away at the rock. When his energy started to falter, he would recite Shingon dharanis, and, grasping his will, his resolve would return. One day, two days, three days in succession Ryokai's efforts continued unabated. Every traveler who passed would laugh derisively at him, but Ryokai's resolve was undaunted. Their laughter only spurred him on and strengthened his resolve to realize his purpose.

Soon Ryokai built a wooden hut near the cliff to protect himself from the rain and damp weather. Every morning he would rise early while the stars were still reflected in the waters of the Yamakuni River and set to work. Every evening he would work until the sound of the river waters echoed from the night sky. But the travelers passing by did not cease to ridicule him with their laughter.

"This fool has no idea of his own limitations," they would say, scornfully, of his efforts. In spite of this, Ryokai worked wholeheartedly with an unswerving sense of purpose. As long as he used his hammer, no worldly thought disturbed his heart or mind. There was no longer any remorse for his past crimes. There was no desire to be reborn in paradise. There was a deep sense of fulfillment found only in the effort made from selfless devotional service. Since his ordination as a monk, the memories of the evil deeds which had previously tormented him were now gradually fading day by day. Because he could see the benefits resulting from the work, his unrelenting resolve grew stronger, and he focused his full concentration on hammering.

A new year arrived. Then spring followed and summer passed; soon the entire year was gone.

Ryokai's efforts had not been fruitless. At one end of the cliff a cave about ten feet deep had been carved out of the rock. Although the cave was small, it demonstrated that Ryokai's indelible mark had been etched on the mountain. The villagers continued to mock Ryokai.

"Look," they said, "that crazy monk has been working all year and only managed to dig out ten feet."

Ryokai, however, looked at the hole and was so delighted with the progress that tears of joy gushed forth. No matter how small the cave, it was a monument to his resolve to realize his spiritual purpose. With each year Ryokai's determination deepened. In the complete darkness of night, and even in the gloom of the cave during daylight, he sat there working his right arm incessantly as if in a frenzy. For Ryokai, the moving of his right arm became the expression of his religious practice, dedicating every action, selflessly, for the benefit of others.

Outside of the cave the sun shone brightly, the moon rose, the rains came and the storms raged, while inside the cave there was only the unbroken clanging of the hammer. Even after two years, the villagers were still jeering. But it had lost its hard edge. Only when they saw Ryokai would they look at each other and giggle. After another year passed, the sound of Ryokai's hammer was heard as unceasingly as the sound of the waters of the Yamakuni River. The village people now were silent. Without their even knowing it, the ridicule and giggling had given way to amazement.

Ryokai had not stopped to shave his head and his ungroomed hair fell upon his shoulders. His unbathed body was covered with the dust of his labors. This all gave him an inhuman appearance. Squirming like a beast in the cave he had carved out for himself, he worked his hammer without stopping, as if he were possessed.

Before they knew it, the villagers' amazement was turning to sympathy. Whenever he needed to go out on his alms round, begging for food, he would unexpectedly find a bowl of food at the entrance to the cave. This allowed him more time for working on the tunnel. So Ryokai now had the time he used to spend on his alms round available to continue his digging.

The end of the fourth year came, and Ryokai's cave was already about 50 feet deep. As compared to the total width of the cliff, however, the depth of the cave was insignificant. Although the villagers were amazed at his efforts and respected his purpose, no one was willing to help because they still believed the project was impossible to complete and thought Ryokai's efforts were in vain. Ryokai continued digging all by himself. He was so absorbed in the digging, however, that he had no thought except to move the hammer. His only thought was to continue his digging for the rest of his life, as if he were a mole. Outside the cave spring went and autumn came and the four seasons changed, while inside, the cave echoed with the unbroken sound of the hammering.

The passing villagers started to pity him: "The poor monk," they would say, "he must have gone mad to continue to dig at that mountain. He'll be dead before he has completed one-tenth of the tunnel." But another year passed and another. At the end of the ninth year, he had completed about forty-four yards. For the first time the villagers from Hida realized that Ryokai's tunnel might possibly succeed. If one skinny monk working all by himself could bore so far in nine years, there was a real possibility that, with more men and more time, they could actually complete the tunnel.

This idea began to grow in the minds of the villagers. Although the people of the seven villages along the Yamakuni River had all rejected Ryokai's request for donations nine years before, they now voluntarily started to collect money for the tunnel. They hired some stonemasons to help Ryokai with the digging. Ryokai was no longer working alone. The lively sounds of many hammers boldly striking the hard volcanic rock started coming out of the cave. But the next year when the villagers measured the cave for progress, they discovered that it was only one fourth of the total distance. Upon discovering this, they started to doubt and get discouraged.

"Even if we get more masons to work here, we'll never complete this task. The priest Ryokai has deceived and tricked us, making us waste our money." Gradually they got tired of the work because the progress seemed so slow. Once again Ryokai was to find himself working alone. One by one the stonemasons gradually stopped coming to help. First one, then another, until one day there was no one else to help with the digging. Although fully aware of this, Ryokai made no effort to chase after them. Without saying a word to anyone, he continued his hammering.

The villagers lost all interest in Ryokai's project. As the cave became deeper, he went further and further from the sight of the travelers passing by as he continued his work. People looked into the dark cave wanting to know if he still existed, saying: "Is priest Ryokai still working?" But soon interest in Ryokai gradually waned until finally Ryokai's existence began to be completely forgotten by the villagers. As his existence became forgotten to the villagers, so the existence of the villagers became unimportant to Ryokai. To him nothing existed except the great wall of rock in front of him.

After more than ten years of his sitting in the dark, cold cave his face was pale, his eyes were sunken, his flesh was so sparse that his bones protruded. He looked more like a ghost than a man. In his heart, however, Ryokai was fully alive; the commitment to his purpose lighted his way. Every inch, or even a fraction of an inch, of the rock that was chipped away would produce a peon of joy.

Another three years passed since Ryokai was left alone, and the villagers once again started to wonder about him. Out of curiosity they measured the cave and found it to be one hundred and thirty yards long. There was now a window overlooking

the river to let in light. One third of the great cliff
had been cut through, primarily by the emaciated
arms of this one old monk.

They were astounded and awestruck. They felt
ashamed of themselves for their former ignorance.
Their respect for Ryokai rose again in their hearts.
Soon the sound of nearly ten hammers from stonemasons hired by the villagers joined the sound of
Ryokai's. Another year passed. The year passed
quickly, before the villagers knew it. They started to
resent paying for something with nothing to show
for it. They feared they were wasting their money.

Again, one by one the hired stonemasons left,
until only the sound of Ryokai's hammer shattered
the silence of the cave. Whether or not there was
anyone working beside him, Ryokai's hammering
did not change. Just like a machine, he worked his
hammer with all his strength. He completely forgot
about himself. The memories of the murder of his
master, the highway robberies, and the other murders, all faded from his thoughts.

Another year passed, and yet another. His
single-minded purpose concentrated his strength.
Even though his arm was thin, it was as unyielding
as iron. By the end of the eighteenth year, before he

realized it, he had completed half of the tunnel's length.

Seeing this awesome miracle, the villagers no longer doubted Ryokai's ability to complete the task. They wholeheartedly repented of having twice withdrawn their support for Ryokai's work. The people of the seven villages got together with the most sincere attitude to help the old monk. In that year a local official of the Nakatsu clan came through the area on an inspection tour and specifically commended Ryokai. Nearly thirty stonemasons were collected from the neighboring area, and the work leapt forward as quickly as fire burning through dead leaves.

Seeing Ryokai's pitifully emaciated body, people urged him to slow down: "You could oversee the work of the stonemasons," they would say. "You needn't do the heavy work yourself." Although they tried to persuade Ryokai to work less, he paid no attention to them. It seemed he would rather die with a hammer in his hand than to slow down now. He simply continued to work as diligently as ever, forgetting occasionally to eat or sleep or even to notice the thirty stonemasons working with him.

It was very natural that people advised Ryokai to take a rest. He had been sitting for nearly twenty years in a rock cave without any sunlight. As a result of the years of sitting, his legs had lost their flexibility, and he had to use his staff for support even on short walks. After all those years in the dark and with his eyes constantly bombarded by stone chips, his eyesight was severely impaired. His eyes were filmed with the milky haze of cataracts, and he could barely distinguish objects.

For all his unstinting purpose, Ryokai now feared the onset of old age and weak health. Although he had no attachment to his body or to life itself, he regretted the idea that he might die while the tunnel was only halfway completed. "Come on, only two more years of exertion," he cried out to himself within his heart. He raised his hammer strenuously trying to forget his age and weakness. The great wall of rock which stood before him with the invincible force of nature had, after all, been carved out by the arm of one worn-out old monk. The cave that now pierced the flank of this mountain seemed like a living thing that would soon pierce the very heart of the mountain and emerge out the other side.

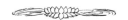

Chapter Four

Although Ryokai's life was endangered by weakness from age and overwork, an even greater threat sought to end his life.

The family of Nakagawa Saburobei had been struck from the registry of clans as a result of the scandal of its lord being killed by his own retainer. If a family could not control its own retainers, it was not worthy of registry. Jitsunosuke, the only son who had been but three years old when his father was killed, had to be brought up by a relative.

When Jitsunosuke was thirteen he first learned about his father's violent death. Especially when he discovered that his father's murderer had not been a samurai of equal rank but only a servant in his father's household, his mind burned with irrepressible rage. From that moment on the idea of vengeance was indelibly engraved in his mind. He entered a Yagyu style fencing academy to learn swordsmanship. At the age of nineteen he was awarded a

certificate of full proficiency in the art of swordsmanship. He set out at once on a journey of revenge.
He was encouraged by his relatives, who promised
to get his family reinstated in the clan registry if he
could be successful in his vendetta.

Jitsunosuke suffered many hardships, being an
inexperienced traveler, as he searched earnestly for
Ichikuro whom he viewed as his enemy. Because he
had never seen him, Jitsunosuke had as much chance
of finding him as he did of capturing a cloud.
Throughout Japan's main island up and down he
wandered year after year in vain, until he was
twenty-seven years old. His hatred was frequently
in danger of being obliterated by the difficulties of
the journey, but when he considered the violent
manner of his father's death and the grave responsibility of reestablishing the house of Nakagawa
Saburobei, then the anger would revive.

Nine years after leaving Edo in the spring of
the year, he found himself in the castle town of
Fukuoka on the island of Kyushu. Since his search
on the main island had been fruitless, he decided to
come south to Kyushu. After leaving Fukuoka, he
went to the castle town of Nakatsu, arriving on a
day in February. He visited the Usa Hachimangu

Shrine, where he prayed that his long-awaited goal might be fulfilled. After praying, he took a rest in the tea house on the grounds of the shrine. By chance, he overheard a conversation between a farmer and a pilgrim: "It seems that the priest was originally from Edo. They say he killed a man when he was young, and later became a monk. He made a vow to work for the salvation of all sentient beings. The tunnel of Hida, which I told you about, was single-handedly carved out by this priest."

When Jitsunosuke heard these words, a rush of elation rose up in him that he had not felt for the last nine years. He asked with excitement: "I want to ask you a question: How old is this priest?"

The man was honored that his conversation had attracted the attention of a samurai. "Well, I've never actually met him, but I've heard people say he is about sixty."

"Is he short or tall?" He followed up one question with yet another.

"I can't be sure about that either. In any event, he stays deep in the cave, so it would be difficult to tell."

"Do you know his secular name?"

"I've never heard it, but he seems to have

been born in Kashiwazaki, Echigo. As a young man he went to Edo. So I've been told," replied the farmer.

This information made Jitsunosuke jump for joy. One of his relatives had mentioned, before he started his journey, that his enemy was a native of Kashiwazaki in Echigo. He might have returned to his native town, so Jitsunosuke should look especially carefully in Echigo.

Jitsunosuke felt this was the answer to his prayer at the Usa Hachimangu Shrine. He was overjoyed by this news. As soon as he was sure of the old monk's name and the directions to the Yamakuni Valley, he started out to track down his enemy, although by that time it was already past two in the afternoon.

Jitsunosuke arrived in the village of Hida around eight in the evening. He thought about going immediately to the cave, but on reflection, decided not to act on his impatience. He decided to wait until the morning to confront his father's killer. He spent a fitful night at the Hida Station Inn. He rose early the next morning, dressed lightly in case he might be fighting, and started out toward the cave.

Upon arriving at the mouth of the cave, he asked one of the stonemasons who was carting out stone chips: "I've heard there is a priest named Ryokai in this cave. Is this true?"

"How could it be otherwise? The priest Ryokai is like the guardian spirit of the cave," laughed the stonemason, insensitively.

Jitsunosuke felt a surge of emotion as he cherished the idea of imminent success. Yet he cautioned himself to be careful.

"Is this the only way out?" he asked. He must not let his enemy escape.

"Where else?" replied the stonemason. "It has been his life's work to create this cave to make a safe passageway through to the other side."

Jitsunosuke rejoiced in his heart to have finally cornered his enemy, like a rat in a trap. No matter how many stonemasons worked for Ryokai, he thought, he would easily be able to kill them all.

"I have a request of you," he asked. "Go tell Ryokai that someone has traveled a great distance to meet him."

Once the stonemason had disappeared into the cave, Jitsunosuke loosened his sword and moistened the rivet on the handle of his sword, in anticipation of the fight. As he did so, he imagined the face of his enemy in this long-awaited confrontation. Although Ryokai was over fifty, he must be strong and muscular to supervise these stonemasons, especially since, as a young samurai, he was a skilled swordsman. Jitsunosuke thought he must stay alert and on guard.

But soon an old monk emerged from the cave in front of Jitsunosuke. It would be more accurate to say that he limped out of the cave like a toad. Nor was his appearance one of a man as much as the remains of one. His flesh had fallen away and his bones stuck out like a skeleton. His legs below the knees were so covered with open sores that it was difficult to look at them without turning away. It was possible to tell he was a monk from his tattered robe, but his hair was long and covered a wrinkled forehead. The old monk blinked his milky colored eyes, looked up at Jitsunosuke and said: "My old eyes are dim with age and failing me. I cannot recognize who you might be, Sir?" When Jitsunosuke saw this pathetic figure, he was shocked and startled. He staggered back as the old monk approached. In his mind he had expected to see an evil priest, one he could hate from the bottom of his heart. Before him crouched a half-dead old monk, neither quite alive nor yet a corpse. Jitsunosuke tried to stir up his emotions, now sunk nearly to despair, by demanding energetically: "Are you the priest Ryokai!?"

"Why, yes, I am," replied Ryokai, dubiously. "And who might you be?"

"Call yourself Ryokai, dress as a priest, you cannot have forgotten that in your youth when you were still called Ichikuro, you killed your master, Nakagawa Saburobei, and ran away. Don't you remember? I am Jitsunosuke, the only son of Saburobei. Prepare yourself for death. There is no escape!"

Although his speech was calm and collected, the threat contained a genuine sternness of purpose.

Ryokai, however, was in no way frightened or surprised.

"Why? Are you really master Jitsunosuke, the son of my master, Nakagawa? Indeed, I am the Ryokai who killed your father and fled." His reply suggested not so much fear at meeting an enemy, as affection for the long lost son of his late master. Jitsunosuke thought that he must be careful not to be fooled by the friendly tone of Ryokai's words.

"I've spent nearly ten years of hardship in tracking you down. You who committed the evil crimes of murdering your master and fleeing from justice. Come out and fight! There is no escape!"

Ryokai remained completely composed. Although he was slightly saddened at the prospect of dying before he had completed his life's work, which he had hoped to complete within the year, he was completely willing to accept death, since this was the consequence of his past misdeeds.

"Master Jitsunosuke, you are welcome to kill me, wretch that I am. You may have heard that I've been digging this tunnel to atone for my past crimes. I've spent nineteen years on it, and it is now nine-tenths completed. Even if I die now, the tunnel will be finished before the year ends. If I die at your hands, and if I shed my blood here at the entrance to this tunnel, I offer up my life for the benefit of others. I have nothing more to regret."

So saying, he blinked his sightless eyes.

As he stood before this half-dead old monk, Jitsunosuke felt the hatred he had harbored against the enemy of his father dissolving into emptiness. In repentance for his father's murder and other crimes, this man had spent half his life in continuous tortuous toil. Now confronted with Jitsunosuke, this "enemy" was meekly willing to die. What possible benefit could there be, Jitsunosuke wondered, to take the life of this half-dead old monk? But if he didn't kill him now, how could he ever end his journey and return to Edo, or ever hope to restore his family's honor? He told himself that he must kill the old monk out of self-interest rather than hatred. To kill out of cold, calculated self-interest without anger was more than Jitsunosuke could bring himself to do. Whipping up a hatred that was quickly dying, he resolved to kill an enemy whose life was not worth taking.

Just at that moment five or six stonemasons came out of the cave. Seeing Ryokai's danger, they surrounded him for protection. They confronted Jitsunosuke with the question: "Just what are you trying to do to Ryokai?" Their faces reflected a clear sign of determination not to allow any harm to come to the old monk if things turned hostile.

"Circumstances have made this old priest my enemy. Now that I have managed to find him, I intend to carry out my long sought revenge. I shall not spare anyone who tries to stop me," said Jitsunosuke sternly.

Although he spoke in a tone of strong determination, in the meantime, the number of stone-masons had increased, and they were joined by several travelers. They all surrounded Jitsunosuke and created an uproar at the idea of any harm coming to their cherished Ryokai.

"To seek revenge might still be possible if the man continued to lead a worldly life. As you can see, he has become a monk, the Reverend Ryokai. He has left the life of the world to become a Buddhist monk. Moreover, he is regarded as the manifestation of the Bodhisattva Jizo* for the seven villages of the Yamakuni Valley," so insisted one of them, meaning that revenge was simply not possible against someone who had been ordained as a Buddhist monk.

Having been challenged by the crowd, Jitsunosuke felt his anger arising again. Because of

---

* Jizo Bodhisattva, Kshtigarbha in Sanskrit, Ti-ts'ang in Chinese, is the Bodhisattva who appears as an ordinary monk, usually holding the wish-fulfilling gem and a monk's staff with six rings; he has vowed to go to the lowest of hells and remain there until all the inhabitants of hell have been released from suffering. He is often venerated as the protector of women, children, animals and travelers.

his warrior's pride, it would be humiliating to withdraw from this place or back off at this point: "I will kill anyone who tries to prevent me from avenging my father's death." With that, Jitsunsuke unsheathed his sword. Everyone surrounding Jitsunosuke resolved to fight. At that point, Ryokai spoke up in his thin, hoarse voice. "Wait! All of you! He is entirely justified in seeking my life. It is precisely because of that crime, that I have been digging this tunnel. It is my dying wish that I should give up my half-dead old body to the hands of this dutiful son. I want no one hurt by standing in the way." As he spoke, he came forward and crept out to stand beside Jitsunosuke.

The people who knew Ryokai understood that his decisions were unshakable once he had made up his mind. It seemed that Ryokai's life must now end. At that moment, however, the leader of the stonemasons stepped forward and spoke to Jitsunosuke.

"You must know," he said, "that Ryokai has devoted his life to the work of carving this tunnel. He has committed himself completely for twenty years of unstinting effort. Although it might be the appropriate consequences for him to die as a result of his past crimes, I feel it is unjust that he should die before his life's work is finished. We respectfully ask you to put Ryokai's life in our care until the work here is completed. As soon as the tunnel is done, you can do whatever you wish to Ryokai."

"This is right! This is right!" shouted the people in support of the chief stonemason.

Jitsunosuke realized that he could not ignore this argument. He might not be able to kill his enemy at the moment because the crowd might prevent it. If he waited until the tunnel's completion, Ryokai—who was quite willing to die now—would surely be bound to surrender his life to Jitsunosuke. Besides these considerations, it would be far better to let this pathetic old monk, even though he was an enemy, complete his life's work. Looking from Ryokai to the crowd and back, Jitsunosuke stated: "I grant your request, out of respect for Ryokai's monastic vows. But do not forget your promise!"

"You won't have to remind me," replied the chief stonemason gently. "As soon as this tunnel breaks through to the other side even by a small hole, then you may kill Ryokai. In the meantime, please stay here at your ease and relax."

Now that the commotion had died down without incident, Ryokai crept back into the tunnel, regretting only that it had wasted precious time.

Jitsunosuke felt greatly disturbed that these unexpected events had frustrated his purpose at the crucial moment. He attempted to control his obvious anger as one of the stonemasons showed him into a small wooden hut. Thinking about the situation now that he was alone, he felt cowardly that he had not been able to carry out his revenge when he met his enemy face to face. Quickly an impatient anger overwhelmed his heart. The generosity that made him agree to let the tunnel be completed before killing his enemy evaporated. He decided on a plan to sneak into the cave that night, kill Ryokai and leave. But the stonemasons kept as close an eye on Jitsunosuke as they did on Ryokai.

The first few days went by in frustrated waiting. On the fifth night he decided the moment had come. The stonemasons had slackened their vigil and had gone deeply to sleep as was their nightly routine. In the middle of the night Jitsunosuke suddenly rose and drew his sword that lay by his bed and stealthily left the hut.

It was early spring, and the moon shone clear, making the waters of the Yamakuni River seem like deep blue whirlpools in its light. Jitsunosuke, however, paying no attention to the beauties of nature, snuck silently toward the entrance of the cave. The sharp stone chips, scattered about the ground, hurt his feet with every step. The cave was completely dark except for the dim glow of moonlight at the entrance and through the windows cut out of the side of the cliff. Feeling his way with his right hand along the side of the wall, he crept further into the cave.

About two hundred and fifty yards into the cave, he began to hear the clanging of a hammer against stone at regular intervals. He did not recognize the sound at first. Then at each step, it grew louder and louder, until finally its echo shattered the quiescence of this sanctuary. He had no difficulty now recognizing the sound of the iron hammer bashing against the rock wall. The eerie sound of the hammer sent a powerful shock of emotion through Jitsunosuke's heart with every beat. As he advanced deeper into the cave, the shattering sound echoed against the rock walls, making a fierce assault upon his ears. Guided by the sound, he crept slowly closer. He intuitively felt that this sound could only be emanating from his enemy, Ryokai.

Stealthily preparing his sword for attack and holding his breath, he advanced. At that moment he heard Ryokai's voice between the blows of the hammer. Partly whispering, partly moaning, he chanted Buddhist scriptures as he worked. This hoarse, sad voice fell on Jitsunosuke's angry heart like a bucket of cold water. In spite of the total darkness of the cave, Jitsunosuke clearly envisaged Ryokai sitting upright in the darkness bashing away at the rock while all nature slept quietly around him. Ryokai's heart/body/mind was no longer human: it was the harmonized heart/body/mind of the bodhisattva going beyond all joy and anger, all emotion with single-minded determination to wield the hammer.

Jitsunosuke realized that the fierce grip he had upon the hilt of his sword had inadvertently slackened. He suddenly became aware of himself. He saw himself sneaking up on this virtuous monk like some highway robber or a predatory beast. He was preparing to draw his sword under the cover of darkness to kill this holy monk who had realized

fully his Buddha Nature and was selflessly undergoing great hardships for the good of other living
beings. A violent shudder shook his entire body.

The powerful echo of the hammering and the
mournful monk's voice invoking the Buddha had
completely shattered his murderous resolve. He
realized that he had no choice now but to honor his
promise and wait patiently for the completion of
the work. Emotionally shaken by this experience,
he crawled out of the cave guided by the glow of
the moonlight at the entrance.

It was not long afterwards that Jitsunosuke in
the form of a samurai could be seen working along-
side of the stonemasons. He had completely given
up the idea of a sneak attack on the old monk and a
quick departure. He realized that Ryokai had no
intention of hiding or trying to escape. Jitsunosuke
decided to wait patiently for Ryokai's life's work to
be completed.

He realized that he might speed up the process,
even if only by a little, if he lent his strength to the
great undertaking. This would be better than standing idly by and doing nothing. As he became aware
of this, he started working along with the stonemasons and started wielding a hammer with them.

The two enemies sat side by side working their hammers. Jitsunosuke worked with all his might hoping that it would allow him to realize his revenge sooner. Ryokai also seemed just as eager to complete his life's work so that Jitsunosuke could satisfy his goal. Redoubling his efforts, almost like a madman, he struck against the face of solid rock.

A month passed, and a new month came. Jitsunosuke, moved by the strength of Ryokai's efforts, found himself forgetting his hatred for his enemy as he focused on the great work of completing the tunnel. Alone at night while the stonemasons slept off the fatigue of the day's work, the two enemies could be found wordlessly hammering away together.

It occurred on September 10th of the third year of the Enkyo Era, the twenty-first year since Ryokai first made a chip with his hammer to start the Hida tunnel, and eighteen months since Jitsunosuke had first met Ryokai. On that night the stonemasons, as was usual, had gone to sleep in the hut while Ryokai and Jitsunosuke were hammering diligently away ignoring the fatigue of the day's work. Around midnight on that night Ryokai's hammer came down with all its strength. It felt as though it had struck rotten wood. The hand holding the hammer carried forward by the force of the blow, smashed into the rock. "Aye!" he cried in sudden surprise. At that precise moment through the small hole made by his hammer, even with Ryokai's cloudy, aged vision, he could see the clear waters of the Yamakuni River shining in the moonlight. Ryokai let out one sudden indescribable cry: "Oh!" His whole body was shaken with a violent shudder, then the entire cave was filled with a tear-filled cry of laughter, as he rolled on the ground like a madman.

"Look, master Jitsunosuke, my great prayer has been answered in an instant after twenty-one years of work!" Ryokai took Jitsunosuke's hand and showed him the waters of the Yamakuni River through the little hole. Just beneath the hole he could see the dark earth of the mountain path running along the riverbank. Hand in hand the two "enemies" sat shedding great tears of joy.

But soon, Ryokai suddenly drew back and said: "Now, master Jitsunosuke, today is the day, please kill me. If I die at this moment of religious joy, I shall certainly be reborn in the Pure Land of the Western Paradise. If you wait until tomorrow, the stonemasons will surely stop you. So kill me now."

His hoarse voice echoed throughout the tunnel. Jitsunosuke, however, could only sit motionless in front of Ryokai with his arms folded, tears streaming down his cheeks. Seeing this old monk's face filled with tears of joy flowing from the very depths of his heart made the idea of killing him inconceivable. His own heart was overflowing, not with any desire for vengeance, but with respect and admiration for the great achievement accomplished by the iron will but feeble hands of this old monk. Crawling toward Ryokai, he took the hands of the old monk in his own once again. Everything forgotten, they sat together and cried with an emotion that went beyond any words that might try to express it.

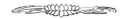

A NOTE ABOUT AO-NO-DOMON
AND THE PRIEST RYOKAI

The story of the priest Ryokai cutting a tunnel through the cliffs of the Yamakuni River valley at Ao is based on historical fact. In 1735 this Buddhist priest asked permission of the feudal lord of Nakatsu to cut a tunnel through this great cliff. Permission was granted, and later he was also allowed to ask for donations from the feudal lords of the entire island of Kyushu. Money was collected. The stonemason Kishino-Heiemon, from Fuchu in Choshu, was hired to supervise the work. The tunnel, now called the Ao-no-Domon, took 15 years to complete. It was finished in the year 1750. The original tunnel was nine feet wide, twelve feet high and had five arched windows facing on the Yamakuni River to the east. In the Meiji era the tunnel was modified three times to its present size and shape. There is now a Buddhist shrine in part of the original tunnel. The newer tunnel has a modern road through it.

Rev. Ryokai was born in Takada, Echigo province; his family name was Fukuhara. Before he became a priest he lived in Asakusa, Edo, which is present-day Tokyo. The story told by Kan Kikuchi is similar to the story recounted on monuments erected in memory of this priest. He died in 1774 at the age of eighty-eight.

He was a 'rokujurokubu' or 'rokubu' which means sixty-six books. It refers to priests who, to this day, carry on their shoulders a stack of sixty-six books of Buddhist scriptures called the Hokekyo. The priests carry these books on their pilgrimage with the stack of books topped by a small roof to protect them from rain. The books are copied to donate at each of the famous places of pilgrimage in all sixty-six provinces of Japan. Pilgrimages are historically a part of Buddhist practice. During the life of the Buddha, he typically walked from town to town, giving out teaching and receiving alms from the householders. Later, property was donated to establish monasteries, and Buddhist monks lived in the monasteries during the rainy season. They traveled from town to town during the dry weather. Both monks and lay people use pilgrimages as a means to deepen their practice and demonstrate the ongoing process of Buddhist training.

Although the part of the story relating to Jitsunosuke Nakagawa may, or may not, be the creation of the author, it was quite common in Japan to have a vendetta, especially if the family was so disgraced by events so as to be removed from the official rolls of families.

The priest Ryokai who created the original Ao-no-Domon collected tolls from travelers who passed through the tunnel, and he used the money for additional works, repairs and improvements. In his later years he carved Buddhist teaching in blocks of stone. At his death he donated money to the Rakanji Temple at Yabakei to have Buddhist sutras read and services performed in his memory and in memory of the building of the tunnel. The doing of memorials in Buddhist practice is used to help both the living and the dead. Merit is gained in the doing of the services and in hearing the scriptures, and that merit is offered for the benefit of others.

LIST OF PHOTOS:

1. *The Yamakuni River and the steep cliffs at Ao.*
2. *Ao-no-Domon - the original tunnel.*
3. *The Buddhist Shrine in the original tunnel.*
4. *Ao-no-Domon - the original tunnel of Ryokai. This shows both old and new tunnels.*
5. *Ao-no-Domon, the tunnel carved by Rev. Ryokai in the 17th century, has been widened and extensively shortened by work in the 19th century. This is how it looks today. It is still providing safe passage for travelers. The cliffs plunge straight down into the Yamakuni River (visible on the left).*

6. *Rakanji Temple in the Yamakuni River Valley where Rev. Ryokai lived for a long time.*

   Rakanji Temple is also pictured on the front cover.

ABOUT THE ORDER OF
BUDDHIST CONTEMPLATIVES

The Order of Buddhist Contemplatives is a religious order prac-
ticing Serene Reflection Meditation (J. Sōtō Zen) as transmitted
from The Very Reverend Keidō Chisan Kohō Zenji, Abbot of Sōjiji
Temple in Yokohama, Japan, to Rev. Master P.T.N.H. Jiyu-
Kennett. Rev. Master Jiyu-Kennett came to the United States in
1969 and established Shasta Abbey in 1970. She founded the Order
of Buddhist Contemplatives in 1978, serving as Head of the Order
until her death in 1996. In North America, the Order now has
Priories in Berkeley and Santa Barbara, California; Eugene and
Portland, Oregon; the North Cascades Buddhist Priory in
McKenna and Seattle, Washington; and the Lions Gate Buddhist
Priory in Vancouver B.C., Canada. In Europe, Throssel Hole
Buddhist Abbey in Northumberland, United Kingdom, was
founded in 1972 and now has branch Priories in Reading and
Telford, United Kingdom. The Order has male and female monks;
women and men have equal status and recognition and train
together in the Buddhist priesthood. All ranks and both sexes are
addressed as "Reverend" and are referred to as both monks and
priests; the monastic order is celibate. In addition to monastics, the
Order includes lay ministers throughout the world. There are also
meditation groups affiliated with the Order through their connec-
tion with Abbeys and Priories in Great Britain, Canada, the United
States, the Netherlands and Germany. The Head of the Order is
Rev. Master Daizui MacPhillamy; its international headquarters
are at Shasta Abbey. The Order publishes *The Journal of the Order
of Buddhist Contemplatives* quarterly.

ABOUT THE MONASTERIES OF THE ORDER

SHASTA ABBEY, located on sixteen forested acres near Mount Shasta city in northern California, is a seminary for the Buddhist priesthood and training monastery for both lay and monastic Buddhists and visitors. It was established in 1970 by Rev. Master P.T.N.H. Jiyu-Kennett, who was Abbess and spiritual director until her death in 1996. Buddhist training at Shasta Abbey is based on the practice of Serene Reflection Meditation and the keeping of the Buddhist Precepts. The monastery is home to 30 to 40 ordained male and female monks and its Abbot is Rev. Master Ekō Little, a senior disciple of Rev. Master Jiyu-Kennett.

Guests and visitors follow a schedule that is similar to that of the monastic community, providing a balance of sitting meditation, work, ceremonial, and instruction in Buddhism. The schedule allows the mind of meditation to be cultivated and maintained throughout all aspects of daily life. Retreat guests stay at the Abbey's guest house, which accommodates about 40 people. All meals are vegetarian and are prepared in the Abbey kitchen. A stay at Shasta Abbey allows visitors to set aside their usual daily concerns, so that they may participate wholeheartedly in the spiritual life of the monastery.

In addition to its monastic and lay training programs, Shasta Abbey offers a Buddhist Supply service and publishes books through Shasta Abbey Press. For more information call or write the Hospitaller, Shasta Abbey, 3724 Summit Drive, Mt. Shasta, California, 96067-9102; phone (530) 926-4208 or fax (530) 926-0428.

THROSSEL HOLE BUDDHIST ABBEY is situated in a quiet valley in the north of England. It was founded in 1972 by Rev. Master Jiyu-Kennett as Throssel Hole Priory, and over the years has become a monastery and seminary for training priests of the Order, as well as a retreat and training centre for a large European congregation. Its

Abbot is Rev. Master Daishin Morgan, a senior disciple of the late Rev. Kennett.

The Abbey offers for lay guests a full and varied programme, to which all are warmly invited. Experienced senior priests teach both meditation and how to use the Buddhist Precepts in establishing a daily practice. Through these means one can find the Truth, or Buddha Nature, at the heart of oneself and all beings. Training shows how to let go of the clinging that causes suffering, thus allowing this inner compassion and wisdom to enrich our lives. Guests meditate in the bright and spacious ceremony hall, and sleep there at night, dormitory-style, with complete privacy between men and women maintained. A large dining hall includes a small library and common room area for guests. By following the monastery's daily schedule, guests experience how it is that all activities of life—working, relaxing, reading, eating and sleeping—have true spiritual depth and value. For more information call or write the Hospitaller, Throssel Hole Buddhist Abbey, Carrshield, nr. Hexham, Northumberland NE47 8AL, United Kingdom; phone +44 (0) 1434 345204 or fax +44 (0) 1434 345216.

ABOUT THE SANTA BARBARA
BUDDHIST PRIORY

The Santa Barbara Buddhist Priory is a temple of the Order of Buddhist Contemplatives. It was founded in the name of Rev. Master Jiyu-Kennett in 1979. The Prior is Rev. Jishō Perry, M.O.B.C. The Priory is a training center and monastic residence with a regular schedule of meditation instruction, daily meditation and services, Buddhist festivals, retreats, and classes in Buddhist practice. The Priory is located at 1115 Tunnel Road, Santa Barbara, California, 93105; phone or fax (805) 898-0848.